Appreciation of Literary Forms

S0-CFN-578

Comprehension Skills

Glenn R. Williston

Jamestown Publishers
Providence, Rhode Island

Comprehension Skills Booklet

No. CB-7M Appreciation of Literary Forms
No. CT-7M Cassette

Cover design by Stephen R. Anthony
Illustrations by Mary M. Macdonald

Printed in the United States   AL
88 9 8 7

ISBN 0-89061-070-3

Readability
Parts One and Two, Lesson: Level F
Part Three, Sample Exercise: Level F
Part Four, Practice Exercises: Levels D—H
Passages 1—6:   Level D   Passages 7—12:   Level E
Passages 13—18: Level F   Passages 19—24: Level G
Passages 25—30: Level H

HOW TO USE THIS BOOK

Without Accompanying Cassette

1. Open to page 7. Complete the Preview Quizzes as you read Part One, Types of Literature.

2. Go on to page 11. Complete the Preview Quizzes as you read Part Two, Figurative Language.

3. Go on to page 25. Read the instructions and complete the Sample Exercise in Part Three.

4. Go on to page 29. Read the instructions and complete the 30 Practice Exercises in Part Four.

5. Correct your answers after each exercise using the key which starts on page 60.

6. Record your progress on the chart on page 64.

With Accompanying Cassette

1. Find Cassette No. CT-7M. The label should read: Appreciation of Literary Forms.

2. Start the recorder and open the book to page 7.

3. Follow the instructions given on the tape and listen to the tape as you complete the Preview Quizzes and read Part One, Types of Literature.

4. Go on to page 11. Listen to the tape as you complete the Preview Quizzes and read Part Two, Figurative Language.

5. Go on to page 25. Listen to the tape as you read the instructions and complete the Sample Exercise in Part Three.

6. Go on to page 29. Listen as you read the 30 Practice Exercises in Part Four. Stop the player after each passage and answer the questions.

7. Correct your answers using the answer key which begins on page 60.

8. Record your progress on the chart on page 64. Start the player again for the next exercise.

INTRODUCTION

The Comprehension Skills Series has been prepared to help students develop specific reading comprehension skills. Each booklet is completely self-contained. There is no separate answer key or instruction manual. Clear and concise instructions are given on page 3 and throughout the booklet to guide the student through the lessons and exercises.

The titles of the Comprehension Skills Booklets also match the labels found on all of the comprehension questions contained in other Jamestown textbooks. Using the appropriate booklet allows the student who is having difficulty with a particular kind of question to gain extra instruction and practice and correct that specific weakness.

Each Comprehension Skills Booklet is divided into four parts.

Part One clearly defines, explains, and illustrates the specific skill discussed.

Part Two offers an interesting and informative lesson presented in clear, readable language, using illustrations from the student's own experience. A simple preview technique is used regularly throughout Parts One and Two; it requires the student to anticipate and respond.

Part Three consists of a sample exercise with four questions. An explanation supporting the correct answers is given as well as reasons explaining where wrong answers are faulty. The sample exercise is designed to prepare the student for the work required in the following section.

Part Four contains 30 practice exercises with questions. Edward Fry's formula for estimating readability was used to grade the exercises. The passages begin at grade 4 and advance gradually to grade 8. The student is advised to complete the 30 practice exercises thoughtfully and carefully. The student is also urged to consult the instructor if extra help is needed before proceeding to Part Four.

An optional tape cassette is available for each Comprehension Skills Booklet. The tapes add an audio dimension to the series and are especially helpful to students who need assistance in comprehending written material. The cassettes help by enlisting the student's listening comprehension ability. All of the instructional matter and exercise paragraphs are recorded on the tape, permitting the student to listen while reading along.

The Comprehension Skills Booklets and optional Cassettes offer a practical and solid program of reading comprehension instruction.

PART ONE

TYPES OF LITERATURE

Preview Quiz 1

As a preview to what will be discussed in Part One, try to answer this question:

Which types of writings may be called "literature"?

☐ a. Only those that are based on adventures
☐ b. All those that stir the imagination
☐ c. Only those that state a point of view

Begin reading Part One to find the correct answer.

One purpose of this booklet is to help you understand the term **literature**. Another purpose is to help you understand figurative language — the special way that writers use words.

In this booklet, we use the term **literature** to include all writings that arouse the emotions and/or stir the imagination. Literature, with its clear and graceful language, appeals to the heart and mind of the reader.

The first literature grew from people's need to entertain themselves. They sat around a great campfire and made up stories to amuse themselves. The writer's purpose today is the same. A writer tries to make you believe that something is happening (the plot) to someone (a character) somewhere (the setting).

Literature also helps us to learn about ourselves and others. It helps us to understand why people act the way they do. It takes us into worlds we may not see otherwise. Literature, then, is a mirror of life. It can be enjoyed by many people, and its ability to entertain continues over the years.

A brief look at several forms of literature might be helpful.

One branch of literature is poetry, or verse. Poetry explores ideas and human emotions. It depends on the natural flow of speech for its beauty and meaning. Poetry, even more than prose (all other kinds of writing), depends on exact wording. That is, a poem says a lot in a little space. The first word of every line of a poem usually begins with a capital letter. Sometimes poems contain rhyme and rhythm like music.

Every other kind of writing that is not poetry is called prose. This, then, is the other major division of writing. Prose divides into two areas: **fiction** and **nonfiction**.

Fiction and nonfiction are really opposites. Nonfiction means real or true. The writer of nonfiction must stick to the facts. Fiction means unreal or untrue. In writing fiction, writers are not limited to the facts. They are free to create their characters and the roles they will play in the story. **Fiction** appeals to the reader's *imagination*. It is about people who do not really exist, events which have never really happened and places which may not be real. Like poetry, fiction may entertain or discuss a truth of life (called the theme) or teach a lesson (called the moral). It is through fiction that we escape from the worries and cares of everyday life and explore new worlds. Fiction makes the unreal seem real. We meet characters and watch them develop. We share their joys and their sorrows. Short stories, novels and plays are examples of fiction.

Nonfiction, on the other hand, appeals mostly to the reader's *mind*. But it too may deal with people, places and events. There is one important difference, however. The people, places and events are real.

A nonfictional writing about a person's life is called a **biography**. If someone writes a story about his or her own life, it is called an **autobiography** (*auto-* means self). Biographies and autobiographies are usually about famous people.

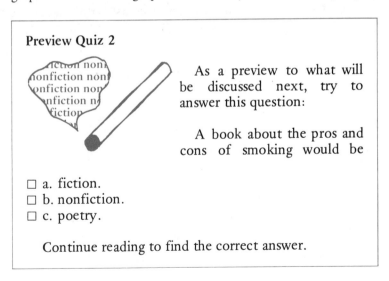

Preview Quiz 2

As a preview to what will be discussed next, try to answer this question:

A book about the pros and cons of smoking would be

☐ a. fiction.
☐ b. nonfiction.
☐ c. poetry.

Continue reading to find the correct answer.

Since nonfiction appeals to the reader's mind, it deals solely with ideas, opinions and attitudes. This type of nonfiction is found in a kind of writing known as the **essay**. In everyday life we call the essay by other names. We talk about articles, reports and "stories."

Through the centuries writers have used the essay to explore many different subjects — from the pros and cons of smoking to the work habits of the ant. In fact, one might say that there is no end to the number of subjects for essays.

The most common example of the essay is found in the daily newspaper. In the newspaper there are news stories, travel reports, book and movie reviews, sports stories and feature stories. Editorials and magazine articles are also examples of essays.

Strictly speaking, the newspaper is not an example of literature. But in this booklet we will refer to the newspaper as such because it plays such an important role in all of our lives.

In all forms of literature, writers often use words in special ways. This is called **figurative language**. Simply stated, it is language that suggests an idea. It is a way of saying something that carries meaning beyond the dictionary definition of each word. It creates special effects and can make ideas clearer. And perhaps most important of all, it makes writing colorful and forceful. Figurative language adds depth and richness to writing.

Part Two explores figurative language in detail. And it discusses many figures of speech commonly found in literature.

You do not need to memorize any of the definitions in this section or in Part Two. It is more important that you understand the literary terms explained in this section and that you become familiar with figurative language as it is discussed in Part Two.

PART TWO

FIGURATIVE LANGUAGE

Preview Quiz 3

As a preview to what will be discussed in Part Two, try to answer this question:

Which one of the following groups of words is the best example of figurative language?

☐ a. Work with pride
☐ b. Boil with anger
☐ c. Sing with joy

Begin reading Part Two to find the correct answer.

This lesson discusses the uses of figurative language in writing. Remember that it is more important to understand figures of speech than it is to memorize them.

We use **figurative language** so much in our daily speech that we do not always know we are using it. We "boil with anger," or an idea "dawns on us." "The years roll by." And a party is a "real blast." We don't stop to say, "Wow! What a great figure of speech." We use these expressions naturally.

Notice that these examples of figurative language are colorful. They add force to what we say. **Literal language,** on the other hand, is dull and colorless. It uses the common, dictionary meanings of words. Of course, we use literal language more than we use figurative language in speech because we wish to be direct and clear in what we say. But, when we wish to color our ideas and add depth to them, we use figurative language.

Let's look at some common phrases which are based on figurative language. Suppose you see your friend coming in out of the rain. You say, "You're a pretty sight. You look a bit damp." His reply is, "Damp! I nearly drowned out there. It's raining cats and dogs!"

Even though you both are speaking in figurative language, you understand each other. You have both been saying something *less* than what you really mean ("You look a bit damp."), something *more* than what you really mean ("I nearly drowned out there. It's raining cats and dogs!") and something *opposite* to what you mean ("You're a pretty sight.").

On the literal level, which uses the common, dictionary meanings of words, the comments make no sense at all. Someone just learning English would not be able to understand what you are saying. You did not mean that your friend was a "pretty sight." Instead, you meant that he looked terrible. You did not really mean that he looked "a bit damp." You meant that he looked very wet. Also, your friend did not mean that he was nearly drowned or that cats and dogs were falling from the sky. So, figurative language makes very good sense on one level, but no sense at all on a different level.

Writers use figurative language for the same reason that we use it in everyday speech: to make ideas clear, colorful and forceful. For example, in a newspaper, we read that Congress has cleared away the "red tape" on a bill. In a magazine article, we read about a dam at the "mouth" of a river. In a novel, we read about someone "inching" her way to safety. In a famous poem, we see fog coming in "on little cat feet." These examples of figurative language are only a few of the many types found in literature.

Preview Quiz 4

As a preview to what will be discussed next, try to answer this question:

Figurative language helps readers

☐ a. to form pictures in their minds.
☐ b. to read faster.
☐ c. to understand big words.

Continue reading to find the correct answer.

It may seem foolish to say one thing and mean another, but, in fact, it is not. Figurative language allows the writer to present ideas clearly and with color. It helps readers to "see" everything they read about to form a picture in their minds. It helps to bridge gaps between ideas.

We can say that figurative language is a way of making unclear ideas clear. It makes the unknown or unreal seem real. For example, a famous writer once described a bat as "a black glove thrown up at the light and falling back." He paints a word picture in figurative language that makes the bat and its flight clear to the reader.

Figurative language can add strong feelings to writing. W. H. Auden is famous for his line, "I'll love you dear, I'll love you/Till China and Africa meet." Notice how much less emotion is shown in the line, "I'll love you, dear, for a long time." So, through figurative language, writers often show emotions and feelings.

We speak of figurative language in terms of figures of speech. So that you will recognize them as you read, they are:

1. Symbol
2. Simile
3. Metaphor
4. Personification
5. Overstatement

6. Understatement
7. Change-of-name
8. Sound-words
9. Alliteration
10. Allusion

Every figure of speech is made in a different way. And each has its own special purpose. It is not important for you to know all the figures of speech. But you should be able to recognize many of them in your reading.

Symbol

One of the most common figures of speech is the symbol. A symbol is used to mean something else. The flag, for example, is the symbol of a country. The wedding ring is a symbol of marriage. And the eagle is a symbol of power and freedom.

In literature some symbols have been used so often that they are known by most readers. The sea is usually a symbol of life. A flower or a butterfly is a common symbol of fragile beauty. A rock is the symbol of strength.

Simile

Similes (and metaphors) compare things. A simile compares things using the words *like, as* and *than.* If you have ever described someone as "slower than molasses" or "faster than lightning," you have used similes.

Preview Quiz 5

As a preview to what will be discussed next, try to answer this question:

Which one of these expressions is a simile?

☐ a. On the spur of the moment
☐ b. Busy as a bee
☐ c. The power and the glory

Continue reading to find the correct answer.

The simile is the most common figure of speech we use. In fact, we depend on similes so much that they become worn-out very quickly. Similes like "cold as ice" or "busy as a bee" have lost their color. Good writers try to create new similes that will express their ideas clearly and interestingly.

In the sentence "Jill swims like a fish," the grace and ease of Jill's movements are compared to the movements of a fish. It would be impossible, in fact, for Jill to swim like a fish. She is human. So in a true sense, the comparison is foolish and not real. However, in a figurative sense, the comparison is perfect. It allows the reader to see Jill's movements clearly.

The reader should be careful when picking out similes. Not every expression using *like, as* or *than* is a simile. "Jack looks like an athlete" is not a simile. Jack is a person to begin with. So there is no real comparison with anything unusual. However, "Jack runs like a panther" is a simile. Two different things are being compared. Notice that the literal sentence "Jack runs very fast" is dull and lifeless by comparison.

To help you to recognize similes in literature, several examples are given below.

From poetry:

> O my love's like a red, red rose.

> . . . the light of her eye, (is)
> Like a star glowing out from the blue of the sky.

From prose:

> The canyon lay waiting for them like a monster, its jaws ready to snap shut on them.

> The doctors were working with their sleeves up to their shoulders and were red as butchers.

Metaphor

The metaphor does not depend on the words *like, as* or *than*. Instead, the metaphor compares two things directly. This makes the metaphor stronger than a simile. We speak of the eyes of a potato, the hands of a clock, pearly teeth, an iron will and so on. We call a person a peach, a rat or a dog. In each case a word usually used for one thing is applied to something else. And in each case the meaning of the word is shifted.

Like similes, metaphors, too, are over-used. Writers try to create fresh metaphors. These give power and excitement to their ideas. One writer described clouds as mounds of whipped cream and mashed potatoes. This description is unusual and striking. It paints a clear word-picture for the reader.

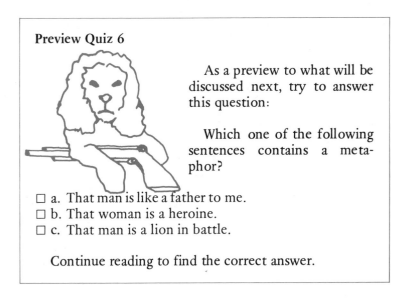

Preview Quiz 6

As a preview to what will be discussed next, try to answer this question:

Which one of the following sentences contains a metaphor?

☐ a. That man is like a father to me.
☐ b. That woman is a heroine.
☐ c. That man is a lion in battle.

Continue reading to find the correct answer.

17

Not all direct comparisons are metaphors. Saying that a person is a hero is not a metaphor. Hero is simply the name for a certain kind of person. But saying that a man is a lion in battle is a metaphor. The man is being compared to a symbol of great strength and bravery, a lion. So, writers try to make their metaphors imaginative and interesting. The following examples may help you understand metaphors.

In the eyes of the law, you're innocent until proven guilty.

The stars were hard little chips of light.

Afraid to move, he was a rigid tree limb on the ground.

Personification

Sometimes an object or an animal is described as if it were human. This is called personification (per SON i fi CA tion). Notice the word *person* in personification. It will help you to remember that personification means treating a thing or an animal as if it were a person. In the sentence "The sun smiled down on the picnickers," the sun is made to seem real. It is a nonliving thing, but it is given a human action. Of course, the sun cannot smile, but in a figurative sense, it can mean warmth, comfort and pleasure.

Sometimes an object is described as though it were an animal, rather than a person. But since the object is made to seem alive, this too is considered to be personification. In the sentence "The car purred along the highway," the car is described as though it were a cat. Another example is: "The ball missed its target and hopped into the street." Strictly speaking, a ball cannot hop. Only animals like rabbits and kangaroos hop. So, personification is used to describe the ball.

Making nonliving things seem alive helps readers to form clear pictures in their minds. We say that "money talks," the wind "whistles through the trees" and the "ocean roars." These expressions make speech and writing more interesting.

Do not confuse natural sounds with human sounds. For example, "the old stairs creaked" is not personification. Stairs do creak. This is natural for them. Creaking is not a human sound. But, "the stairs groaned under our weight" is personification since only living things can groan. The following are examples of personification:

> The dark cave closed its angry jaws on the lost explorers.

> The fence by the house leaned wearily toward the road.

Overstatement

Overstatement is the name for *exaggeration* in literature. It is used so often that we have come to expect it. It is a natural part of colorful speech and writing. For example, we often say, "I'm starved" or "I'll die if I don't pass this exam" or "I have a million things to do." We exaggerate to make what we wish to say stronger. We draw attention to our comments by overstating them. Writers use overstatement for the same reason — to draw attention to their ideas.

Preview Quiz 7

As a preview to what will be discussed next, try to answer this question:

An overstatement is a statement which

☐ a. should not be accepted as fact.
☐ b. is a lie that fools the reader.
☐ c. is found only in scientific reports.

Continue reading to find the correct answer.

Like all figures of speech, overstatement may be used many ways. It may be serious or humorous. It may entertain or prove a point. Ralph Waldo Emerson once wrote, "Here once the . . . farmer stood/And fired the shot heard round the world." He was trying to stir the pride and patriotism of his countrymen. Literally, of course, a shot could not be heard around the world, and the reader should not accept this statement as fact. Emerson did not expect his readers to believe his statement. The exaggeration catches the reader's attention and shows the importance of the first battle of the war.

Even though overstatement should not be accepted as fact, the reader must remember that overstatement is not a lie. A lie twists the truth for the purpose of tricking. The reader should remember also that overstatement, like other figures of speech, is found in all types of writing. The only place where figures of speech are not found is in scientific reports where clear-cut, literal language is used.

Understatement

Understatement is the opposite of overstatement. But oddly enough, it serves the same purpose. It gets the reader's attention and adds color to ideas. Understatement uses language which is *opposite to* what is expected or which is *less than* what is expected. Readers fill in the truth themselves.

For example, we might read that "Last night was the coolest night of the winter. At 7 A.M. this morning the temperature was ten below zero." In this example, the word *cool* is clearly an understatement.

The American writer Artemus Ward once said that a man who holds his hand for a half hour in a fire will feel great warmth. This statement is a good example of understating, or saying less than, the truth.

Change-of-Name

Change-of-name is the use of one word to represent something else, or part of something else. For example, a writer may say, "Washington is hoping for an early end to the war." When the writer uses the word "Washington," she really means officials of the U.S. Government. Here, she is using the name of a place to stand for a group of people. This is possible because over the years people have come to connect the word "Washington" with the idea of the U.S. Government, so that now this word can be used as a substitute. Another example of this is the word "Moscow." Today, when we hear this word, we usually think of the Soviet Government instead of the city itself.

Change-of-name can also mean using the name of part of something when we really mean the whole thing. For example, at a cattle sale, buyers talk about taking so many "head." Although the head is only part of a cow, you know right away that the buyers are talking about the whole cow. In recent years, "wheels" has come to mean car.

Preview Quiz 8

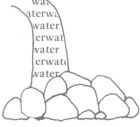

As a preview to what will be discussed next, try to answer this question:

Which of the underlined words sounds like the action itself?

☐ a. My mother is the <u>kindest</u> person in the world.
☐ b. The tire went flat when we drove over <u>broken</u> glass.
☐ c. The water <u>hissed</u> as it dripped on the heated rocks.

Continue reading to find the correct answer.

Sound-Words

Some words sound like the thing they are describing. Examples are "buzz," "crunch," "tinkle," "gurgle," "sizzle," "hiss," "splash" and "crash," to mention just a few. From Edgar Allan Poe we have the lines "Hear the . . . Silver bells/ How they tinkle, tinkle, tinkle,/In the icy air of night." Sound-words are like fine spices. They are used sparingly to add flavor and richness to writing.

Alliteration

Alliteration (a LIT er Ā tion) is the name for a group of two or more words which begin with the same sound. This figure of speech is often used to create a mood or feeling. The following examples will make this figure of speech clear:

The *s*weet *s*cent of *b*urning *b*ark . . .

The *f*orest's *f*erny *f*loor . . .

Into the *d*eep, *d*ark, *d*ungeon . . .

Allusion

An allusion is a reference to something. A writer may mention something from history, quotations from the Bible or from literature, names of places or current events. A character in a story, for example, might say that someone is older than Methuselah. Methuselah was a person in the Bible who, we are told, lived more than 900 years. The character, in a figurative sense, seems to be more than 900 years old. Notice that this example of allusion is also a weak simile and a strong overstatement. Figures of speech do mix together often. Trying to tell them apart is not necessary. It is more important to be able to see the differences between literal and figurative language.

Summary

These steps can help you to understand figurative language:

1. Look for things that are compared.

2. Notice words used in unusual ways.

3. Check for words which seem to be taking the place of other words.

4. Look carefully at the words on each side of a figure of speech to help you understand its meaning.

5. Listen to the sounds of words, especially in poetry.

6. See if the wording makes sense literally. If it doesn't, it is probably figurative language.

Computers, which can be "trained" to understand literal language, are often confused by figurative language. One such computer translated the expression "out of sight, out of mind" into "invisible, insane." Do not make the same mistake when you read.

The exercise which follows this lesson is designed to help you understand the uses of literary forms and figures of speech. Read it carefully and refer back to these pages if necessary.

PART THREE

SAMPLE EXERCISE

The exercise on the next page is a sample exercise. Its purpose is to show you how the information you have studied in Parts One and Two is put to use in reading.

A second purpose of the sample exercise is to show you how to do the 30 exercises which appear in Part Four. Reading the sample exercise and answering the sample questions will help you to get off to a good start.

All the answers to the four questions are fully explained. Reasons are given showing why the correct answers are best and where the wrong answers are wrong.

Complete the sample exercise carefully. Do not go on to Part Four until you are sure you understand literary forms.

Sample Exercise

Life aboard a whaling ship in the 1800s was not always exciting. Often, when whales were few and hard to find, the days were slow and boring. Still, there were always small jobs to pass the time. Also, there was reading, writing letters and scrimshaw. When at last whales were sighted, the cry of "Thar she blows!" would set off the excitement of another chase. Although the days could be dull, night brought the real loneliness. Darkness coiled around the ship like a great sea serpent. It was brightened only by the few whale-oil lamps burning below deck. The men, who were not on watch, sat or curled up on bunks as narrow as coffins. The lucky ones slept. Their lullaby was the creak and squeak of timbers and the rumble of the waves.

1. This paragraph is an example of
   - □ a. poetry.
   - □ b. fiction.
   - □ c. nonfiction.
   - □ d. biography.

2. Which one of the following sentences contains a simile?
   - □ a. Life aboard a whaling ship in the 1800s was not always exciting.
   - □ b. The men, who were not on watch, sat or curled up on bunks as narrow as coffins.
   - □ c. It was brightened only by the few whale-oil lamps burning below deck.
   - □ d. The lucky ones slept.

3. In this paragraph the writer
   - □ a. develops characters.
   - □ b. teaches a lesson.
   - □ c. creates an exciting plot.
   - □ d. builds setting and mood.

4. Underline the first example of figurative language in the paragraph.

Answers and Explanations

1. The best answer to the first question is *c*. The paragraph is an example of nonfiction. Since the paragraph discusses a true subject — life aboard a real whaling ship in the 1800s — nonfiction has to be the correct answer.

Answers *a, b* and *d* are wrong for these reasons:

Answer a: Poetry has a special set-up very different from the paragraph form of this selection.

Answer b: Fiction deals with people, events and places that were created by the writer's imagination. Whaling did exist in the 1800s. Since the selection is based on fact and only fact, it cannot be considered fiction.

Answer d: Biography is a description of a person's life. No person is mentioned in the paragraph.

2. The best answer to the second question is *b*. "Narrow as coffins" is a simile. The bunks are compared to coffins.

Answers *a, c* and *d* are wrong for these reasons:

Answer a: This statement is an opinion without a comparison.

Answer c: This literal statement does not offer any comparison.

Answer d: This brief sentence is a combination of fact and opinion. It offers no comparison.

3. The best answer to the third question is *d*. The writer builds setting and mood. The whole paragraph is concerned with life aboard the ship. This is setting. Words like *slow, boring, dull, loneliness, darkness, coffins,* and so on create mood.

Answers *a*, *b* and *c* are wrong for these reasons:

Answer a: No characters are mentioned in the paragraph. The writer speaks only of "the men" which is too general to be considered character.

Answer b: The paragraph is about life aboard a whaling ship. There is no lesson to be learned.

Answer c: The only hint of plot in the paragraph is the sighting of whales, but this is not developed. It is only mentioned as a welcomed event on whaling ships.

4. The best answer to the fourth question is "Darkness coiled around the ship like a great sea serpent." This is a simile in which darkness is compared to a serpent through the use of the word "like."

If you had difficulty answering these questions correctly, look over the paragraph and questions again. If, after that, you still do not understand the answers and explanations, check with your teacher before going on.

PART FOUR

PRACTICE EXERCISES

The 30 practice exercises which follow will give you a chance to put your knowledge of literary forms to work.

Each exercise is just like the sample exercise you did in Part Three.

Read each passage well and answer carefully the four questions with it. Correct your answers using the answer key at the back of the book. Record your progress on the chart on Page 64 before going on to the next exercise.

Practice Exercise No. 1

At the rim of the forest stood a birchbark wigwam. Inside there was a fire that had burned down to a few coals. An old man dressed in a wolfskin robe sat by the fire. His hair was white like frost, and his face was wrinkled.

The old man took a stick from the heap beside him and put it on the fire. In the glare of the blaze, his face looked as yellow as dried willow leaves. Wisps of smoke made shadows on the roof. Outside the wind howled.

Twilight and darkness came, and still the old man sat. Before morning he had put his last stick on the fire. "When this has burnt, the fire will die," he said. He rested his head on his arm and mumbled, "And with it, so will I."

1. The final paragraph can be seen as
   - ☐ a. a study of nature.
   - ☐ b. a death watch.
   - ☐ c. an error in judgment.
   - ☐ d. a basic truth of life.

2. The second paragraph
   - ☐ a. appeals mostly to the reader's sense of hearing.
   - ☐ b. introduces a character.
   - ☐ c. develops a mood of suspense.
   - ☐ d. predicts what will happen to the old man.

3. Which one of the following sentences contains a figure of speech?
   - ☐ a. The old man took a stick from the heap beside him and put it on the fire.
   - ☐ b. In the glare of the blaze, his face looked as yellow as dried willow leaves.
   - ☐ c. Wisps of smoke made shadows on the roof.
   - ☐ d. Twilight and darkness came, and still the old man sat.

4. In two sentences nonliving things are given living qualities. Underline either one of these examples of personification.

Practice Exercise No. 2

One April morning high above the plateau, two black dots appeared. Wispy clouds played tag across the blue sky. The black dots grew larger and larger.

Spring had arrived in all her glittering beauty. The snowy blankets covering the high mountain peaks were shrinking up the slopes. And trickles of water grew to raging rivers. A mule doe lifted her head from grazing and looked at the bald eagles. At first she was concerned for her fawn, but the birds were not flying a hunting pattern. They were flying in a single direction. They were traveling. Finally, the two dots flew low enough to see the doe and a rabbit playing in the morning sun. But the two birds had other interests. They were looking for the nest they had been using for twenty years.

1. Which sentence is an example of personification?
   - ☐ a. Wispy clouds played tag across the blue sky.
   - ☐ b. A mule doe lifted her head from grazing and looked at the bald eagles.
   - ☐ c. They were flying in a single direction.
   - ☐ d. But the two birds had other interests.

2. The sentence "Spring had arrived in all her glittering beauty" shows that
   - ☐ a. the writer knows little about the seasons.
   - ☐ b. a simile is an interesting figure of speech.
   - ☐ c. a nonliving thing can be made to seem alive.
   - ☐ d. spring is the writer's favorite season.

3. The thread of action which runs through the selection is
   - ☐ a. the grazing of the mule doe.
   - ☐ b. the gathering of clouds.
   - ☐ c. the melting of snow.
   - ☐ d. the flight of the eagles.

4. Underline the first sentence which appeals to the reader's sense of sight.

Practice Exercise No. 3

A jay went walking into a yard where peacocks once lived. There he found several feathers which had fallen from the peacocks. He gathered them all together and tied them to his tail. Then he strutted down toward the peacocks in the nearby yard. When he came near them, they looked at him strangely. After studying him from a distance, they soon discovered the cheat. Walking up to him, they pecked and plucked away his borrowed plumes. So the jay was forced to go back to the other jays. They had watched his foolish actions from a distance, and they were also upset with him. They clicked their tongues as they told him, "Fine feathers do not make fine birds."

1. An allegory is a story which depends on many symbols. A parable is a story from the Bible. A fable is a story in which animals act like people. A legend is based on an event in the past. This selection may be considered
    ☐ a. an allegory.   ☐ c. a fable.
    ☐ b. a parable.   ☐ d. a legend.

2. The peacocks plucked away the jay's feathers because
    ☐ a. they were jealous of him.
    ☐ b. he was pretending to be something he was not.
    ☐ c. they wanted their old feathers back.
    ☐ d. he was making fun of them.

3. This selection may be called a complete story because
    ☐ a. it is interesting.
    ☐ b. it has a moral.
    ☐ c. it contains figurative language.
    ☐ d. it has a beginning, a middle and an end.

4. Underline the sentence which expresses the lesson or moral of the paragraph.

Practice Exercise No. 4

The airplane struck the surface of the sea with a sound like the slap of a giant hand on the water. Two sharp bumps, and the plane settled quietly back on the long, slow waves. I had made a good landing. I knew that our small bomber would not float long. It is fairly easy to set a land plane down on water, but these heavily laden planes are not supposed to float. I did not intend to stay with it very long. I quickly jumped onto the left wing to receive the life raft from a crewman. He was there to hand it to me without a second's delay. My radioman, who was also my gunner, raised himself from the rear cockpit and was busy with his gear. I was already trying to open the raft's gas valve which at first seemed to stick. Finally, a great woosh of gas inflated the raft and I knew at that moment we would make it.

1. The action of this story is set
   - ☐ a. in a war zone.
   - ☐ b. in the North Atlantic.
   - ☐ c. on Lake Michigan.
   - ☐ d. near a small island.

2. Which one of the following sentences contains a simile?
   - ☐ a. The airplane struck the surface of the sea with a sound like the slap of a giant hand on the water.
   - ☐ b. Two sharp bumps, and the plane settled quietly back on the long, slow waves.
   - ☐ c. I had made a good landing.
   - ☐ d. I knew that our small bomber would not float long.

3. The last sentence contains an example of
   - ☐ a. a sound-word.
   - ☐ b. a change-of-name.
   - ☐ c. a simile.
   - ☐ d. a metaphor.

4. Underline two words which support the answer to question No. 1.

Practice Exercise No. 5

Joan did not want to go in, but she had to. Her mother would be angry if she returned home with the groceries. "Take these few things over to poor Mr. Watson and never mind the foolish stories people tell about him," her mother told her. But Joan did mind. The wind whistled around the old house and blew leaves in her face. Black clouds gathered in the evening sky and warned of an approaching storm. Joan held the bag of groceries tightly in one hand and knocked timidly on the door with the other hand. She heard a loose shutter bang against an upstairs window. She knocked again and held her breath, hoping no one would answer. As she was about to turn and leave, the door squeaked open and a voice from deep within the darkness said, "Come in, my dear, if you dare."

1. Which sentence is an example of personification?
   - ☐ a. The wind whistled around the old house and blew leaves in her face.
   - ☐ b. She heard a loose shutter bang against an upstairs window.
   - ☐ c. Joan did not want to go in, but she had to.
   - ☐ d. But Joan did mind.

2. This selection is probably the first paragraph of
   - ☐ a. a true story about a famous person.
   - ☐ b. a science report.
   - ☐ c. a mystery story.
   - ☐ d. a booklet about the weather.

3. Several sentences in the selection
   - ☐ a. are similes.
   - ☐ b. are based on historical facts.
   - ☐ c. tell about Joan's childhood.
   - ☐ d. appeal to the reader's senses.

4. Underline a sentence in which Joan's actions show her feelings.

Practice Exercise No. 6

Paul "Shorty" Michaels had been "the little guy" all his life. He was the shortest guy in kindergarten, the shortest guy at camp and now the shortest guy on the basketball team.

"Come on, Shrimp, let's see what you can do," yelled John Brigand, a player.

"Why don't you shut your mouth and play ball!" Shorty snapped back as the team went through some drills.

In his early years, being the little guy hadn't hurt Shorty on the basketball court. But as the years went by, some of the other boys began to catch up with him in the basic skills.

"I'm not fooling myself," he had said to his friend Roger Taggert one day. "I'll never play hoop again."

"Why not?" asked Roger. "You could always hold your own with anyone."

Two days later Paul was out on the floor practicing all his old routines, getting ready for the big challenge.

1. Which one of the underlined words is an example of figurative language?
   - ☐ a. "Why don't you shut your mouth and play <u>ball</u>!"
   - ☐ b. Two days later Paul was out on the <u>floor</u> practicing . . .
   - ☐ c. "I'm not <u>fooling</u> myself," he said to his friend . . .
   - ☐ d. "Come on, <u>Shrimp</u>, let's see what you can do."

2. The last four paragraphs
   - ☐ a. suggest that Paul was a superior athlete.
   - ☐ b. build setting and mood.
   - ☐ c. give background information.
   - ☐ d. provide good examples of figurative language.

3. The writer develops the character of Paul as
   - ☐ a. a poor sport who cannot take a joke.
   - ☐ b. a happy and friendly young man.
   - ☐ c. a determined young man with courage.
   - ☐ d. a loner who does not make friends easily.

4. Underline a change-of-name word for basketball.

Practice Exercise No. 7

MARCH 10. This morning a dozen deer came to breakfast. I had made friends with a brown deer on one of my moonlight walks last winter. Cold winters make for few meals. So I sometimes put out apples or pellets of horse feed. I've rubbed the deer's forehead and scratched her nose. I named one buck fawn "Little Guy." Guy Imus was very pleased. Just before dawn a few days ago I was awakened by the noise of yips, yaps, and howls. Slinging a shawl over my nightgown, I ran outside. Suddenly I found myself face-to-face with a great yellow coyote, who greeted me with a sad howl. I answered as best I could and then put on proper clothes to investigate. I soon found the answer. There lay one of the deer, almost completely eaten. I felt sorrow, of course, but this experience gave me yet another lesson in nature's ways — survival of the fittest.

1. This selection is best described as
   - ☐ a. a diary entry.
   - ☐ b. a biography.
   - ☐ c. a news story.
   - ☐ d. a business letter.

2. The setting of the action is probably
   - ☐ a. a small city in California.
   - ☐ b. a seaport in Norway.
   - ☐ c. a lonely weather station in the Arctic.
   - ☐ d. a wildlife area of Alaska.

3. Which one of the following sentences contains an example of "touch" imagery?
   - ☐ a. This morning a dozen deer came to breakfast.
   - ☐ b. Cold winters make for few meals.
   - ☐ c. So I sometimes put out apples or pellets of horse feed.
   - ☐ d. I've rubbed the deer's forehead and scratched her nose.

4. Underline the moral of the selection.

Practice Exercise No. 8

What's new in hotels? For a start, there's rental by the pound! Recently, the new 24-story McCormick Inn of Chicago was renting rooms to weekend guests by weight. A large scale was placed in the lobby, and guests weighed in at seven cents a pound. Women wearing wigs were granted a one-pound discount on their bills. A half pound was subtracted for anyone wearing false teeth or false eyelashes. Any couple with a combined weight of less than 150 pounds was given a room free.

Also new are guest-room movies. This idea has now spread to many hotels around the world after proving successful in the U.S. The idea is called "Pik-a-Movie." By merely clicking the dial on the television set, guests can watch first-run films. At the Sahara Hotel in Las Vegas, four motion pictures in any four-day period are free.

1. This selection is probably part of
   - ☐ a. a book review.
   - ☐ b. a travel folder.
   - ☐ c. a short story.
   - ☐ d. a news story.

2. This selection is written in a style which
   - ☐ a. informs and entertains the reader.
   - ☐ b. complains about hotel management.
   - ☐ c. warns the reader about poor hotels.
   - ☐ d. offers several good figures of speech.

3. The function of the last paragraph is
   - ☐ a. to describe something new offered by hotels.
   - ☐ b. to let the reader know about his rights in hotels.
   - ☐ c. to prove that some hotel rooms cost too much.
   - ☐ d. to add humor to a serious writing.

4. Underline a sentence which appeals to the reader's sense of hearing.

Practice Exercise No. 9

Very early in the morning, about four o'clock, if I listen well, I can hear the rumbling, click, clack, click of the train wheels as they go across the Williamsburg Bridge. About that time, if it is a foggy morning, I can hear the deep booming sounds of the foghorns as the boats go by on the river. With the trains and boats I can also hear the buses pulling in and out of the bus stops. In my apartment I can hear the floor boards squeak as I walk around. It's like this until 6 A.M. Then I can hear the milk trucks as they deliver milk. I can hear the sound of the rattling of the wheels on the push carts as they are pushed to Avenue C. The thing that makes the most noise is the electric company letting out steam from huge chimneys. It sounds like a jet flying overhead.

1. In this selection the writer
   □ a. uses symbols and allusions.
   □ b. creates suspense through a character's actions.
   □ c. makes the trains and buses seem alive.
   □ d. appeals to the reader's sense of hearing.

2. Which one of the following contains sound-words?
   □ a. . . . if I listen well, I can hear the rumbling, click, clack, click of the train wheels . . .
   □ b. . . . I can also hear the buses pulling in and out of the bus stops.
   □ c. . . . I can hear the milk trucks as they deliver milk.
   □ d. The thing that makes the most noise is the electric company . . .

3. The final sentence of the paragraph
   □ a. shows that the writer is blind.
   □ b. proves that the selection is about New York City.
   □ c. hints that the selection is from a short story.
   □ d. contains a simile.

4. Underline a sentence which does not support the answer to question No. 1.

Practice Exercise No. 10

From the very start of that awful lifesaving course, I was a marked woman. The rest of the young learners were small, slender maidens. But I was the large type. I was very big for my fourteen years. And I weighed as much as a grown-up woman. So I was, as the teacher said, the perfect "victim."

The first few days of the course were terrible for me. But they were not very dangerous. In elementary lifesaving, you hold up the drowning person with one hand while you paddle with the other. You are supposed to wrap your arm around his neck and shoulders. This is supposed to keep his head well above the water. All this is very well in theory. But the trick that none of Miss Flowgill's little girls could master was keeping the victim's nose and mouth above the water line.

1. The word *victim* in the first paragraph is enclosed in quotation marks because it is
   □ a. an understatement.
   □ b. the most important word in the paragraph.
   □ c. part of a simile.
   □ d. the exact word used by the teacher.

2. This selection is probably part of
   □ a. an essay.
   □ b. a health report.
   □ c. a biography.
   □ d. an autobiography.

3. The purpose of the first paragraph is
   □ a. to develop minor characters.
   □ b. to give background information.
   □ c. to develop suspense and excitement.
   □ d. to give a detailed description of setting.

4. Write two words which support the answer to question No. 2.

_____   _____

Practice Exercise No. 11

The worst air-pollution disaster in history happened in England during the week of December 5, 1952. A blanket of thick smog covered London. Part of the problem was the smoke from chimneys and smokestacks. The other factor was the unchanging weather. For many days the air did not move. Dust and gases hung like a great, gray cloud over the city. Buses and cars moved along the streets like snails. People tried to find their way through the streets. Their eyes hurt and tears dripped down their cheeks. One person said he felt as though he had been peeling a bag of onions. The air gagged people and left a horrible taste in the mouth. During a five-day period, four thousand people died as a result of the smog.

1. The opening sentence may be seen as
   ☐ a. an overstatement.
   ☐ b. an understatement.
   ☐ c. a factual statement.
   ☐ d. a fictional statement.

2. A metaphor is used in which of the following sentences?
   ☐ a. A blanket of thick smog covered London.
   ☐ b. The other factor was the unchanging weather.
   ☐ c. People tried to find their way through the streets.
   ☐ d. Their eyes hurt and tears dripped down their cheeks.

3. Which one of the following sentences does not contain a figurative comparison?
   ☐ a. Dust and gases hung like a great, gray cloud over the city.
   ☐ b. Buses and cars moved along the streets like snails.
   ☐ c. Part of the problem was the smoke from chimneys and smokestacks.
   ☐ d. One person said he felt as though he had been peeling a bag of onions.

4. Underline two examples of words or expressions which present a mood of darkness and gloom.

Practice Exercise No. 12

Before he was seventeen, Stormalong was famous in the North Atlantic. For one thing, Stormalong was clever and strong enough to harpoon four whales at one time. Naturally, when the whales heard about this young sailor, they all headed for the North Pole. There they could hide under the icecap.

But there were lots of other things in the seven seas to keep a growing lad busy. There was the giant octopus with arms thirty feet long. Stormy had pried these loose from his ship's anchor. Then there was the huge squid. Of course, without a knife, Stormy had a little trouble with him. More to his liking was the bareback ride to China on the biggest white whale ever seen in the Pacific Ocean. Yes, Stormy was quite a lad.

1. A myth deals with gods and goddesses and their super-human feats. A tall tale is based on exaggeration. A parable is a story from the Bible. A "whodunit" is a mystery story that asks who committed the crime. This story is
   ☐ a. a myth.   ☐ c. a parable.
   ☐ b. a tall tale.   ☐ d. a "whodunit."

2. Stormy's strength and deeds are examples of
   ☐ a. overstatement.
   ☐ b. understatement.
   ☐ c. factual description.
   ☐ d. scientific observation.

3. The expression ". . . when the whales heard about this young sailor . . ." represents
   ☐ a. a serious comment in a humorous writing.
   ☐ b. a desire to give the whales special abilities.
   ☐ c. an error in reasoning and judgment.
   ☐ d. an attempt to fool the reader.

4. Underline the sentence in the second paragraph which best supports the answer to question No. 1.

Practice Exercise No. 13

Ben Franklin laid his quill pen on the ink-stained desk — a blue-black journal of the past. He held up his new copybook and ran his eyes over the neatly written words. There might be other fine copybooks in Mr. Brownell's school, but his had poetry on the first page. Ben liked his new school. His father had sent him to Mr. Brownell after he had spent almost a year at the South Grammar School. Mr. Franklin had been forced to give up the hope that Ben would be a minister. His family was a large one, and the candlemaker would not be able to save enough money for Ben's college education. So the boy could not prepare for the ministry. This being the case, there was no reason for him to study Latin. It would be better to put him in Brownell's school. There he would learn to write good English and do ciphering — arithmetic.

1. This selection is probably part of
   - ☐ a. an essay.
   - ☐ b. a biography.
   - ☐ c. a legal document.
   - ☐ d. a fictional story.

2. The writer develops the character of young Franklin as a person who is
   - ☐ a. unhappy with his new school.
   - ☐ b. friendly with other students.
   - ☐ c. proud of his work.
   - ☐ d. honest with his father.

3. Which one of the following sentences contains a metaphor?
   - ☐ a. Mr. Franklin had been forced to give up the hope that Ben would be a minister.
   - ☐ b. Ben Franklin laid his quill pen on the ink-stained desk — a blue-black journal of the past.
   - ☐ c. Ben liked his new school.
   - ☐ d. So the boy could not prepare for the ministry.

4. Underline a sentence which supports the correct answer to question No. 2.

Practice Exercise No. 14

The beagle dog is a sportsman. The thrill of the chase gives zest to his life. Whenever he catches the scent, his bell-like notes resound until they ripple and ring across the fields. He is the music maker of the meadows.

The beagle tracks pheasant and squirrel, but rabbits are his specialty. Their scent is very delicate and their ways, clever. Yet the beagle can unravel the trickiest trails and make corners as quick as any cottontail.

Back in the time of King Arthur, this small, floppy-eared dog hunted rabbits for the King and his knights. Later, when Elizabeth I was Queen of England, she wanted to change the beagle. She had him bred smaller and smaller until she could carry one around in a glove. The hunting squires of her day would fill their saddlebags with these tiny hounds and turn them loose on the heath to go a-hunting.

1. Which of the following contains sound-words?
   - ☐ a. The thrill of the chase gives zest to his life.
   - ☐ b. Whenever he catches the scent, his bell-like notes resound until they ripple and ring across fields.
   - ☐ c. The beagle dog is a sportsman.
   - ☐ d. Later, when Elizabeth I was Queen of England, she wanted to change the beagle.

2. The phrase "music maker of the meadows" is
   - ☐ a. a blend of metaphor and alliteration.
   - ☐ b. a perfect example of literal description.
   - ☐ c. an appeal to the reader's sense of sight.
   - ☐ d. an allusion to an event in history.

3. This selection is probably
   - ☐ a. a first act of a play.
   - ☐ b. a book review.
   - ☐ c. a short essay.
   - ☐ d. a fictional writing.

4. Underline a sentence which appeals to the sense of hearing.

Practice Exercise No. 15

It seemed like Mother Nature was sure kind that day when the little black colt came into the range world. It tried to get a footing with its long, wobbly legs on the brown prairie sod. Short stems of new green grass were trying to make their way up through the last year's faded growth. They were reaching for the sun's warm rays. There was no day, time or place that could beat that morning on the sunny side of the low prairie where Smoky the colt was foaled.

"Smoky" wouldn't have fit the colt as a name just then because he was born jet black. But that name wasn't given to him until he was a four-year-old. He didn't see the first light of day through any box stall window. And there was no human around to make a fuss over him. In fact, the only company he had that first morning was his watchful mammy.

1. Which one of the following contains personification?
   - ☐ a. It seemed like Mother Nature was sure kind that day when the little black colt came into the range world.
   - ☐ b. It tried to get a footing with its long, wobbly legs on the brown prairie sod.
   - ☐ c. "Smoky" wouldn't have fit the colt as a name just then because he was born jet black.
   - ☐ d. He didn't see the first light of day through any box stall window.

2. This selection is probably
   - ☐ a. the final paragraphs of a biography.
   - ☐ b. the opening paragraphs of a book.
   - ☐ c. an article from a magazine.
   - ☐ d. a front page story from a newspaper.

3. The action described in this selection happens during
   - ☐ a. summer.   ☐ c. winter.
   - ☐ b. fall.   ☐ d. spring.

4. Underline a sentence which supports the answer to question No. 3.

44

Practice Exercise No. 16

On a cool winter day in 1823, a boy of 11 entered a London café called Johnson's. He seated himself in the best dining room. When the waiter arrived, the boy asked him for the special of the day. Then he unwrapped a piece of bread he had brought with him and began to gulp down his noon meal. Later he gave the waiter a halfpenny tip.

In the evening, the boy went to visit the debtors' prison where his father was. Sick at heart, the boy returned to his lonely attic room later in the evening. For his evening meal he gnawed on some cheese and a bit of bread.

Charles Dickens was the boy. And about 27 years later these experiences became the subject of his two famous novels *David Copperfield* and *Oliver Twist*.

1. The purpose of this selection is to develop the character of young Dickens as
   - ☐ a. a rude and cowardly son.
   - ☐ b. a deeply religious boy.
   - ☐ c. a brave and concerned young man.
   - ☐ d. a friendly and honest person.

2. This selection is probably from
   - ☐ a. a biography.
   - ☐ b. a diary entry.
   - ☐ c. an autobiography.
   - ☐ d. an essay.

3. In the second paragraph the verb *gnawed* is well chosen because it shows that Dickens
   - ☐ a. was hungry and poor.
   - ☐ b. was in a hurry to leave.
   - ☐ c. shared his food with others.
   - ☐ d. enjoyed his meals.

4. Circle the paragraph which best supports the correct answer to question No. 1.

45

Practice Exercise No. 17

The sea urchin is a living pincushion. Countless tiny spines cover its small, ball-like body. It has spiny feet and five jaws that serve as teeth. This tiny creature buries itself in the sand and hides in rocks. Divers must watch carefully for this danger. If they don't, they may have to spend painful hours with tweezers, plucking spines from their feet.

Coral is a danger, too. It is so colorful that divers are eager to pull off pieces of it. But every kind of coral scratches. Many kinds are poisonous, also. One famous Hawaiian coral diver says, "Never go after coral without wearing heavy gloves. Coral is a deadly trap. It will tear you to pieces and even poison your body. Beware of its beauty."

1. In the first sentence, the writer calls the sea urchin "a living pincushion." This is an example of
   □ a. a literal statement.
   □ b. a proven fact.
   □ c. an alliteration.
   □ d. a metaphor.

2. This brief essay is based on the theme that
   □ a. nature provides man with all his needs.
   □ b. the sea is man's last frontier.
   □ c. a thing of beauty is sometimes dangerous.
   □ d. nature controls the fate of man.

3. The direct quotation in the last paragraph
   □ a. gives factual support to the essay.
   □ b. proves that writers must research all their material.
   □ c. does not agree with the facts given in the first paragraph.
   □ d. suggests several safe ways of finding sea urchins and coral.

4. Underline an example of figurative language in the last paragraph.

Practice Exercise No. 18

Duck-watching is a fascinating sport in early spring. Buy, borrow or beg a canoe and find a wooded stream. You may come upon some of the most beautiful ducks found anywhere — the North American wood duck. You may discover them resting on a pond in the heart of the forest. The male wood duck is like a rainbow. He is the dude among ducks. His head is decorated with a feather crest that seems to be combed straight back. White lines run along the sides of its head. His breast is rust or chestnut-colored, spotted with white. His back is patterned in rich, dark colors.

Wood ducks are found only in North America, and most of them in the United States. In September or October they migrate south, wintering in areas from Virginia to the Gulf of Mexico and the West Indies. Then, in early spring, they migrate back north.

1. The writer's use of color to describe the ducks suggests that
   - ☐ a. the best figures of speech are found in nonfiction.
   - ☐ b. the writer describes everything in terms of colors.
   - ☐ c. setting is made real through colors.
   - ☐ d. images of the senses add interest to nonfiction.

2. Which one of the following sentences contains a metaphor?
   - ☐ a. White lines run along the sides of its head.
   - ☐ b. Then, in early spring, they migrate back north.
   - ☐ c. You may discover them resting on a pond in the heart of the forest.
   - ☐ d. His head is decorated with a feather crest that seems to be combed straight back.

3. In this selection the writer
   - ☐ a. presents strong opinions.
   - ☐ b. stirs the reader's emotions.
   - ☐ c. uses the advice of experts.
   - ☐ d. shows an interest in wildlife.

4. Underline a simile in the first paragraph.

47

Practice Exercise No. 19

About fifteen miles below Monterey, on the wild coast, the Torres family had their farm. A few sloping acres beneath their land was a cliff that dropped to the brown reefs and to the hissing white waters of the ocean. Behind the farm the stone mountains stood up against the sky. The farm buildings huddled like little insects on the mountain skirts, crouched low to the ground as though the wind might blow them into the sea. The little shack and the rattling, rotting barn were grey-bitten with sea salt until they had taken on the color of the granite hills. Two horses, a red cow and a red calf, half a dozen pigs and a flock of lean chickens stocked the place. A little corn was raised on the slope. And it grew short and thick under the wind.

1. In this paragraph the writer seems to be most interested in
   - ☐ a. developing characters.
   - ☐ b. introducing setting.
   - ☐ c. teaching a lesson (moral).
   - ☐ d. telling a truth of life (theme).

2. Which one of the following expressions is an example of figurative language?
   - ☐ a. A few sloping acres
   - ☐ b. The color of granite hills
   - ☐ c. Grey-bitten with sea salt
   - ☐ d. Up against the sky

3. The writer bases his description on
   - ☐ a. logical reasons.
   - ☐ b. exact literal language.
   - ☐ c. historical and biblical allusions.
   - ☐ d. an appeal to the reader's senses.

4. Underline a sentence which contains a simile.

Practice Exercise No. 20

If Rip Van Winkle awoke today after a sixty-year sleep, he would be surprised. The world has changed because of science. We now have skyscrapers, a flood of cars, a great network of roads, a fleet of jets and great achievements in space. Everything would amaze him. And as he looked more closely at the modern household, he would be equally surprised by the inventions that make life easier. Color TV, radio, telephones and all the electronic gadgets that are so important today would seem like miracles. We now live in an age of science. Yet very few people know much about science. Most people are familiar only with things that they can see. The true scientist has little or no thought of his work being applied in the home.

1. The mention of Rip Van Winkle, a character created by Washington Irving, is an example of
   - ☐ a. a strong simile.
   - ☐ b. a literary allusion.
   - ☐ c. a good opinion.
   - ☐ d. a change-of-name.

2. Which one of the following expressions is an example of figurative language?
   - ☐ a. A flood of cars
   - ☐ b. All the electronic gadgets
   - ☐ c. A fleet of jets
   - ☐ d. Great achievements in space

3. The sentence "Everything would amaze him" is best called
   - ☐ a. a figurative statement.
   - ☐ b. an overstatement.
   - ☐ c. an understatement.
   - ☐ d. a literal statement.

4. This essay paragraph is based mostly on opinions. Underline a sentence which comes closest to being fact.

Practice Exercise No. 21

When in 1908 a check for $500 came from Harvard University for my first year as a scholarship student, I was one of the happiest people in the world. Never before had I owned so much money at one time. I was as free as a bird to spend it tracing the words and music of cowboy songs — my project. Excited and eager, I made plans to travel the following summer throughout the cattle country.

It proved a long and hard road that I had started on. I made my way, on foot, on horseback, by buggy, by train, by car. It was a tough journey that has since wound a half-million miles into every part of the U.S. Few of my friends in the University of Texas showed sympathy or took the project seriously. For them cowboy music — this crude product of the West — had no interest, no value, no charm at all.

1. The purpose of the first paragraph is
   - ☐ a. to introduce a plot.
   - ☐ b. to describe setting in detail.
   - ☐ c. to give background information.
   - ☐ d. to present a moral.

2. The sentence "It proved a long and hard road that I had started on" means that
   - ☐ a. by 1908 roads were paved in the West.
   - ☐ b. dirt roads are often filled with ruts.
   - ☐ c. the West was larger than the writer had expected.
   - ☐ d. the work turned out to be difficult and tiring.

3. A truth of life that can be seen in the final two sentences is that
   - ☐ a. man is basically greedy.
   - ☐ b. man is often selfish.
   - ☐ c. at times man must work alone.
   - ☐ d. the enemies of man are everywhere.

4. Underline an example of figurative language in the first paragraph.

Practice Exercise No. 22

It is a world jamboree, a three-ring circus, and the world's busiest airport, all rolled into one big ball. Airplanes flock in like great birds coming home for their yearly reunion. Thousands of them come, their bright yellows, reds, blues and whites stretching toward the horizon like a field of flying flowers. A tent city explodes beside the runway. People sleep in tents, campers, cars and trucks. Some even sleep under airplane wings like cats getting out of the rain.

Where does all this happen each August? At the annual fly-in festival in Oshkosh, Wisconsin, fun-flying capital of the world. Oshkosh is a magnet that draws pilots and non-pilots from all over the world. Everyone who comes to the festival has been bitten by the flying bug. They can't resist walking, looking and talking. There are no strangers at the friendly Oshkosh festival.

1. In the opening sentence the writer
   □ a. seems to be confused.
   □ b. shows the excitement of the festival.
   □ c. presents a truth of life.
   □ d. uses literal language only to describe the event.

2. Which one of the following sentences contains a simile?
   □ a. People sleep in tents, campers, cars and trucks.
   □ b. They can't resist walking, looking and talking.
   □ c. Some even sleep under airplane wings like cats getting out of the rain.
   □ d. There are no strangers at the friendly Oshkosh festival.

3. The phrase "Oshkosh is a magnet" is meant to be
   □ a. a literal statement.
   □ b. a figurative statement.
   □ c. a scientific fact.
   □ d. a foolish comment.

4. Underline a sentence in the first paragraph which contains animal imagery.

Putting your best face forward is sometimes hard after you reach age 11. It's about this time that acne may become a problem. In fact, 60 to 90 percent of all teen-agers have some problem with acne, or skin rashes.

Skin specialists have learned a lot about the causes and treatment of acne during the last ten years. They have found, for example, that acne isn't caused by too much oil coming to the surface of the skin, but by plugged-up oil-gland openings. These openings, or pores, are too small during the teen years to allow all the oil to reach the surface of the skin. The result is acne. Washing the affected areas with soap and water helps the condition. Using a vitamin E ointment helps to heal acne over a period of time.

1. To get the reader's attention, the writer begins the first paragraph with
   ☐ a. a serious statement.
   ☐ b. a shocking fact.
   ☐ c. a logical reason.
   ☐ d. a humorous comment.

2. This selection is probably from
   ☐ a. a news story.
   ☐ b. a magazine article.
   ☐ c. a short story.
   ☐ d. a romantic novel.

3. This selection makes use of
   ☐ a. many sound-words.
   ☐ b. factual, literal language.
   ☐ c. humorous understatement.
   ☐ d. similes and metaphors.

4. Underline a sentence in which the writer gives advice.

Practice Exercise No. 24

Our first attempt at sending up a payload in our rocket was a disaster. It was not because the rocket failed to fire, but because of a nervous passenger. Let us say here and now that we do not recommend sending hornets up in rockets. In other words, we had barely started our new hobby, and already payload rocketry was beginning to bug us.

Insects are not the only payloads waiting to be launched. They are, of course, easily found. And your kid sister is less likely to be attached to a bug than to something like a mouse. But there's really no point in sending up mice, frogs or higher animals, including kid sisters. The speed and jolts would be too much. You could end up with something dead.

1. When the writer describes the hornet as a "nervous passenger," he is being
    □ a. realistic.   □ c. humorous.
    □ b. literal.   □ d. factual.

2. In which one of the following sentences is there a word with double meaning?
    □ a. Our first attempt at sending up a payload in our rocket was a disaster.
    □ b. In other words, we had barely started our new hobby, and already payload rocketry was beginning to bug us.
    □ c. They are, of course, easily found.
    □ d. The speed and jolts would be too much.

3. This selection takes the form of
    □ a. a letter about summer vacation.
    □ b. a personal essay about toy rockets.
    □ c. an introduction to a short story about insects.
    □ d. a biography entry about hobbies.

4. Write two words which prove that the writer is a character in the selection.

_____   _____

Practice Exercise No. 25

The water had risen now to their shoulders. Philip, the young man who had designed this submarine's radar gear, lowered his head until his chin touched the water, rippling it a little. "How long do you think it will be before it's up to . . . here?" he asked, lifting one hand to touch the steel hull just above their heads.

David, the pilot of the tiny, experimental deep-ocean submarine, looked at the tape measure he had set up when they first discovered that the boat was leaking. "About an hour."

Philip lowered his hand, and, not looking at David, said, "And then we drown?"

David didn't answer.

"Unless," Philip said, "they can get the divers down here and then tie a cable to us and lift us up. Is that what they're doing?"

"They can't," David said. "We're down a thousand feet."

"They can't do anything to help us?"

David turned to look at him. "No!"

1. The writer captures the reader's interest by using
   □ a. a great many facts.
   □ b. an interesting form of overstatement.
   □ c. an appeal to all the reader's senses.
   □ d. a mood of suspense.

2. The form of this selection suggests that it was taken from
   □ a. a short story.   □ c. a biography.
   □ b. an essay.   □ d. a play.

3. The theme of this selection could be that
   □ a. man is able to control his own fate.
   □ b. man is a lonely creature.
   □ c. man is helpless against the forces of nature.
   □ d. man is often tempted by evil.

4. Underline an expression which clearly fixes where the action takes place.

For more than 350 years, fishermen have worked the famous Georges Bank, a gloomy gray devil-trap in the North Atlantic. Always dangerous, always a challenge, the bank has yielded large catches of cod, haddock, flounder, and 70 or so other kinds of fish from the cold ocean deep. It has been called "the richest fishing ground in the world." It helped make fishing America's first industry. It inspired wonderful legends of "iron men in wooden ships." As romantic as it may seem, however, fishing the Georges Bank is no sport for an amateur. Icy, 80-mile-an-hour winds carve a lot of character in a man.

The Georges Bank fisherman of today has more to contend with than storms at sea. He is faced with a serious problem that may destroy his way of life. "Forget the *Captains Courageous* romance," says Hugh O'Rourke, director of the Boston Fisheries Association. "Fishing is a business, and we've got problems. To put it simply, the Georges Bank is in danger of being fished out."

1. *Captains Courageous* is the name of a famous novel. So, we may call the reference to this novel
   □ a. a symbol.   □ c. a simile.
   □ b. a literary allusion.   □ d. a change-of-name.

2. The phrase ". . . the famous Georges Bank, a gloomy gray, devil-trap . . ." is an example of
   □ a. a metaphor.   □ c. sound-words.
   □ b. personification.   □ d. a simile.

3. This selection may be called
   □ a. science fiction.   □ c. a biography.
   □ b. nonfiction.   □ d. a short story.

4. Underline the first example of figurative language in the paragraph.

Practice Exercise No. 27

On the map of the world it is only a speck — this eastern island off the coast of Massachusetts. It lies separated from land by 30 miles of water. The Indians gave it a name meaning "Faraway Land." Nantucket, both the island and the town, has such a quaint and rugged nature that residents call it "the real America in miniature." Built by Quakers 300 years ago, it was and still is different from anywhere else. In summer a wave of tourists sweeps upon the island, swelling the population from 4,200 people to nearly 16,000.

What is the special attraction? To put it the way Nantucketers do, "Living here is like being a million miles from the mad, mad world." The time to get to know the people who live here is from October to May. Nantucketers call it offseason, when the cool sea winds crisscross the moors, when distant foghorns sound beyond the shoals, when the herring gulls stand guard on the lonely wharf roof tops.

1. The phrase ". . . a wave of tourists sweeps upon the island . . ." is an example of
   ☐ a. sound-words.   ☐ c. an allusion.
   ☐ b. understatement.   ☐ d. a metaphor.

2. The sentence "The Indians gave it a name meaning 'Faraway Land' " may be seen as
   ☐ a. a good example of personification.
   ☐ b. a simple literal statement.
   ☐ c. a typical figure of speech.
   ☐ d. an allusion to the Bible.

3. The purpose of the first paragraph is
   ☐ a. to give historical background.
   ☐ b. to discuss some of the customs of Nantucketers.
   ☐ c. to convince the reader to visit Nantucket in the fall.
   ☐ d. to describe the island as a good place to live and work.

4. Underline an expression which appeals to the reader's sense of hearing.

Practice Exercise No. 28

Only a dark outline of the train could be seen as it sped through the night. Even the clicking of the iron wheels against the rails seemed oddly soft. And the black smoke hung close as if shielding a friend from his enemy. The locomotive's headlight was turned off and the single coach was unlighted. What strange secret did this train hold?

Abraham Lincoln, newly elected President of the U.S., was the secret passenger. On February 11, 1861, Mr. Lincoln was traveling from Springfield, Illinois, to Washington, D.C., when it was learned that an attempt to take Mr. Lincoln's life would be made in Baltimore. When the party reached Harrisburg, Pennsylvania, a quick change in plans was made. They would leave Harrisburg ahead of schedule aboard a different train. Hours later in Baltimore a would-be assassin stood in the station scratching his head and wondering what had happened.

1. This selection is probably from a
   - ☐ a. romantic novel.
   - ☐ c. magazine article.
   - ☐ b. work of fiction.
   - ☐ d. diary.

2. The purpose of the first paragraph is
   - ☐ a. to create a mood of mystery and suspense.
   - ☐ b. to provide important background information about Lincoln.
   - ☐ c. to suggest that Presidents often find themselves in danger.
   - ☐ d. to illustrate a truth of life.

3. The figures of speech in this selection are particularly well chosen because
   - ☐ a. they are related to historical facts.
   - ☐ b. they teach a lesson.
   - ☐ c. they are based on images of the senses.
   - ☐ d. they stand for justice.

4. Underline a simile in this selection.

Practice Exercise No. 29

Slowly, silently, now the moon
Walks the night in her silver shoes.
This way, and that, she peers, and sees
Silver fruit upon silver trees.
One by one the windows catch
Her beams beneath the silvery roof.
Couched in his kennel, like a log,
With paws of silver sleeps the dog.
From their shadowy shelter the white shapes peep
Of doves in a silver-feathered sleep.
A harvest mouse goes scampering by,
With silver claws and a silver eye.
And moveless fish in the water gleam,
By silver reeds in a silver stream.

1. In this poem
   - ☐ a. someone has a dream.
   - ☐ b. there are many metaphors.
   - ☐ c. the moon is personified.
   - ☐ d. night is called a "dark lady."

2. A reading of this poem reveals that
   - ☐ a. every other line rhymes.
   - ☐ b. the entire poem is one long sentence.
   - ☐ c. literature can be humorous.
   - ☐ d. letter sounds create special effects.

3. The final two lines of the selection are meant to be an example of
   - ☐ a. a simple description.
   - ☐ b. a complex symbol.
   - ☐ c. an historical allusion.
   - ☐ d. an understatement.

4. Underline the only simile in the poem.

Practice Exercise No. 30

"The noise shook green apples off the trees, moved a frog onto the railroad track and caused hens in a poultry yard to lay premature eggs in fright." These words were written in 1885 by a newspaperman who had watched a gathering of fifers and drummers in Hartford, Connecticut.

Fifers and drummers have banded together for generations, mostly in New England, in units known as Ancient Fife and Drum Corps. They are called "ancient" because the history of fife and drum corps goes back in time many hundreds of years. The instruments known as "fifes" are usually made of wood as they were centuries ago. On the other hand, a modern marching band contains many brass instruments and has only a few drummers to provide simple rhythm and a ruffle now and then.

1. The quotation by the newspaperman in the first paragraph
   ☐ a. contains several good examples of similes.
   ☐ b. blends two different ideas.
   ☐ c. sets the stage for characters.
   ☐ d. is based on overstatement.

2. A reading of this selection helps the reader
   ☐ a. to understand some differences between fife and drum corps and modern marching bands.
   ☐ b. to realize that Connecticut is the center of fife and drum corps activity.
   ☐ c. to understand how figures of speech are used effectively in fiction.
   ☐ d. to learn about American customs and traditions.

3. This selection probably comes from
   ☐ a. a biography.   ☐ c. a letter.
   ☐ b. a novel.   ☐ d. a magazine.

4. Underline a sentence which contains the only example of sight imagery in the selection.

Answer Key

Practice Exercise No. 1
1. b   2. c   3. b
4. Outside the wind howled. OR, "When this has burnt, the fire will die," he said.

Practice Exercise No. 2
1. a   2. c   3. d
4. One April morning high above the plateau, two black dots appeared.

Practice Exercise No. 3
1. c   2. b   3. d
4. Fine feathers do not make fine birds.

Practice Exercise No. 4
1. a   2. a   3. a
4. bomber, gunner

Practice Exercise No. 5
1. a   2. c   3. d
4. Joan held the bag of groceries tightly in one hand and knocked timidly on the door with the other hand. OR, She knocked again and held her breath, hoping no one would answer.

Practice Exercise No. 6
1. d   2. c   3. c   4. hoop

Practice Exercise No. 7
1. a   2. d   3. d
4. I felt sorrow, of course, but this experience gave me yet another lesson in nature's ways — survival of the fittest.

Practice Exercise No. 8
1. b   2. a   3. a
4. By merely clicking the dial on the television set, guests can watch first-run films.

Practice Exercise No. 9
1. d   2. a   3. d
4. It's like this until 6 A.M.

Practice Exercise No. 10
1. d   2. d   3. b
4. I, me

Practice Exercise No. 11
1. c   2. a   3. c
4. disaster; thick smog; smoke; great, gray cloud; Dust and gases

Practice Exercise No. 12
1. b   2. a   3. b
4. More to his liking was the bareback ride to China on the biggest white whale ever seen in the Pacific Ocean.

Practice Exercise No. 13
1. b   2. c   3. b
4. There might be other fine copybooks in Mr. Brownell's school, but his had poetry on the first page.

Practice Exercise No. 14
1. b   2. a   3. c
4. Whenever he catches the scent, his bell-like notes resound until they ripple and ring across the fields. OR, He is the music maker of the meadows.

Practice Exercise No. 15
1. a   2. b   3. d
4. Short stems of new green grass were trying to make their way up through the last year's faded growth.

Practice Exercise No. 16
1. c   2. a   3. a
4. Paragraph No. 2

Practice Exercise No. 17
1. d   2. c   3. a
4. Coral is a deadly trap. (metaphor) OR, It will tear you to pieces (overstatement)

Practice Exercise No. 18
1. d   2. c   3. d
4. The male wood duck is like a rainbow.

Practice Exercise No. 19
1. b   2. c   3. d
4. The farm buildings huddled like little insects on the mountain skirts, crouched low to the ground as though the wind might blow them into the sea.

Practice Exercise No. 20
1. b   2. a   3. d
4. The world has changed because of science. OR, We now have skyscrapers, a flood of cars, a great network of roads, a fleet of jets and great achievements in space. OR, We now live in an age of science.

Practice Exercise No. 21
1. c   2. d   3. c
4. I was as free as a bird to spend it tracing the words and music of cowboy songs — my project.

Practice Exercise No. 22
1. b   2. c   3. b
4. Airplanes flock in like great birds coming home for their yearly reunion. OR, Some even sleep under airplane wings like cats getting out of the rain.

Practice Exercise No. 23
1. d   2. b   3. b
4. Washing the affected areas with soap and water helps the condition. OR, Using a vitamin E ointment helps to heal acne over a period of time.

Practice Exercise No. 24
1. c   2. b   3. b
4. Our, we, us

Practice Exercise No. 25
1. d   2. a   3. c
4. this submarine, experimental deep-ocean submarine, down
   a thousand feet, they can get the divers down here and
   then tie a cable to us and lift us up.

Practice Exercise No. 26
1. b   2. a   3. b
4. For more than 350 years, fishermen have worked the
   famous Georges Bank, a gloomy gray devil-trap in the
   North Atlantic.

Practice Exercise No. 27
1. d   2. b   3. a
4. when distant foghorns sound beyond the shoals

Practice Exercise No. 28
1. c   2. a   3. c
4. And the black smoke hung close as if shielding a friend
   from his enemy.

Practice Exercise No. 29
1. c   2. d   3. a
4. Couched in his kennel, like a log,
   With paws of silver sleeps the dog.

Practice Exercise No. 30
1. d   2. a   3. d
4. "The noise shook green apples off the trees, moved a frog
   onto the railroad track and caused hens in a poultry yard
   to lay premature eggs in fright."

Progress Chart

Practice Exercise Number	Put an X Through the Number of Each Question Answered Correctly				Total Number Correct
	Question	Question	Question	Question	
1	1	2	3	4	
2	1	2	3	4	
3	1	2	3	4	
4	1	2	3	4	
5	1	2	3	4	
6	1	2	3	4	
7	1	2	3	4	
8	1	2	3	4	
9	1	2	3	4	
10	1	2	3	4	
11	1	2	3	4	
12	1	2	3	4	
13	1	2	3	4	
14	1	2	3	4	
15	1	2	3	4	
16	1	2	3	4	
17	1	2	3	4	
18	1	2	3	4	
19	1	2	3	4	
20	1	2	3	4	
21	1	2	3	4	
22	1	2	3	4	
23	1	2	3	4	
24	1	2	3	4	
25	1	2	3	4	
26	1	2	3	4	
27	1	2	3	4	
28	1	2	3	4	
29	1	2	3	4	
30	1	2	3	4	

Total of Correct Answers for All 30 Exercises:

Rating: 100 − 120 Excellent
 80 − 100 Good
 60 − 80 Fair